COLLAGE and KEEP

For Emily

F

FRANCES LINCOLN LIMITED
PUBLISHERS

THis bOoK Belongs to

COLLAGE YoUR NAMEHERE

Collage and Keep Contains fifty-two projects for you to CREATE your own visual DIARY.

Respond to the projects in an order that feels best for you, completing ONE at a time or having multiple activities on the go.

Your response TODAY may be different from TOMORROW, so however you choose to CREATE it will reflect your personal JOURNEY. Above all, enjoy!

The Basic Principles of Collage

PHOTOCOPY material to avoid DESTROYING the original, ESPECIALLY precious things like old photographs.

Get a good CRAFT KNIFE and replace your blade REGULARLY.

Photograph items you want to include and print them out.

Use a strong GLUESTICK. Cheaper ones will come unstuck eventually.

◆◆◆◆◆◆◆◆◆

To start your own collection of EPHEMERA, keep your eyes peeled in charity shops and in flea markets, as well as online.

◆◆◆◆◆◆◆◆◆

PORTRAIT
different
yourself

Do you ever wish you could BOTTLE a MOMENT?

Tell the STORY of your favourite RECORD

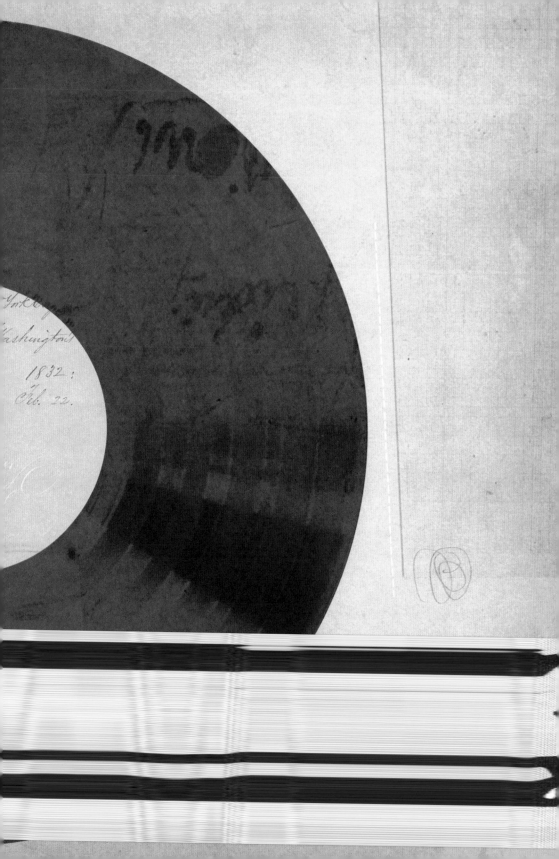

York City

Washington

1832 :
Feb. 22.

Create falling LEAF shapes of THINGS you want to LEAVE behind

leave

What does the FUTURE hold for you?

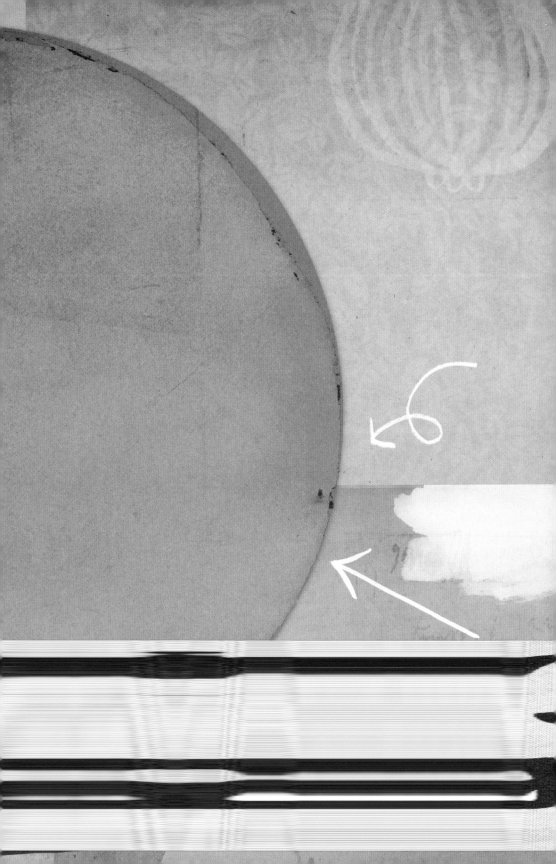

Fill the CABINET full of things that you are CURIOUS about

When you were YOUNGER
what did you want to be?

II.2

No
An
LUCI

ANGE
You
An
ISABE
Wh
An
Fou

Had

Fill the frames with photos of FRIENDS and FAMILY

Create your perfect VIEW

Plant things you want
to see GROW in your LIFE

haHaHa

Who or what makes you LAUGH?

COLLAGE yourself as a SUPERHERO

MAdRe

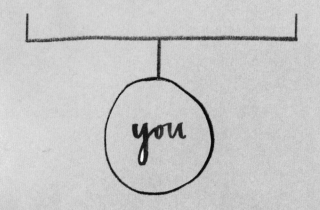

you

Create your own FAMILY TREE

FRÈre

WHAT PATH ARE YOU ON?

Where does the
ROAD less
travelled
lead?

Who or what are your major HANG UPS?

Fill the page with BRIGHT IDEAS

REDESIGN
the covers of
your favourite BOOKS

Who would get an INVITATION to your ultimate DINNER PARTY?

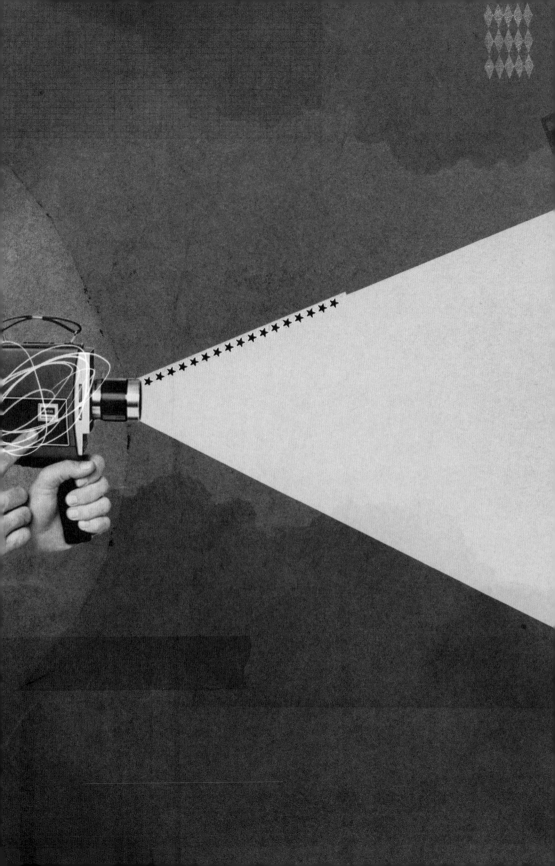

Make a PATCHWORK collage collected from

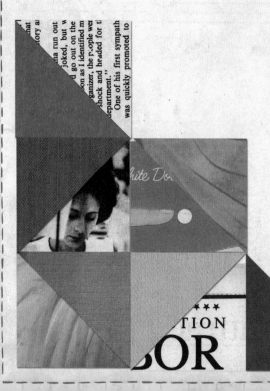

tion
OR

quilt using ephemera you've

iends and family

Fill this room with your FEARS, PHOBIAS and things you HATE

Create signs using good ADVICE you've received

BE KiND

reLaX

What Nourishes you?

CREATE FOOTPRINTS

Using photos of places you've been

YOU

How much do you have in Common?

Fill this page with THINGS that are your FAVOURITE COLOUR

Prix : 23 fr.

Prix : 23 fr.

Collage a PAPERCHAIN of people you connect with

Collage key events from your life to show your JOURNEY

What are *your* GOOD HABITS?
- - - - - - - - - - - - - - - - - -

What are your BAD HABITS?

How did *you*
see the
WORLD as
a child?

THEN

NOW

How do
you see the
WORLD
now?

Collage SECRET THINGS on these pages, and then Sew them SHUT

Fill the lamp with WISHES

What makes you feel safe and protected

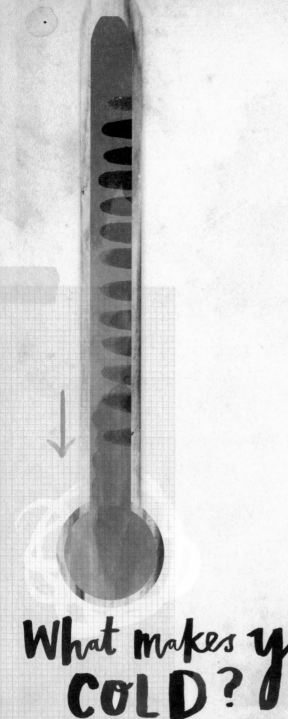

What makes **you**
COLD?

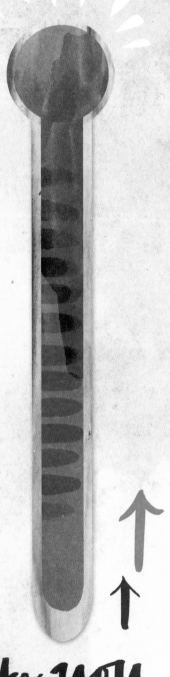

What makes **you**
HOT ?

Pack **ONLY** your most *Areasured* Possessions for the **DESERT ISLAND**

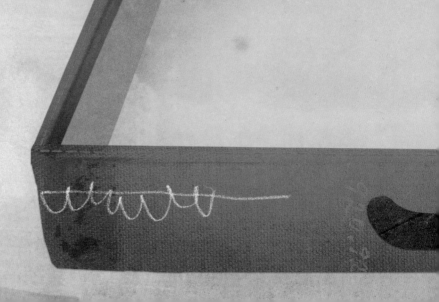

Make balloons
out of photos from
SPECIAL and
HAPPY occasions

you go HERE

If you were **WORLD** LEADER for a day, what would **you** CHANGE?

What do you see whe

What would you like to understand more CLEARLY?

What makes you

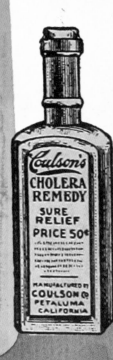

Coulson's
CHOLERA
REMEDY
SURE
RELIEF
PRICE 50¢

MANUFACTURED BY
COULSON CO
PETALUMA
CALIFORNIA

FEEL BETTER?

Create a secret DEN

What do you see through the
KEYHOLE?

→

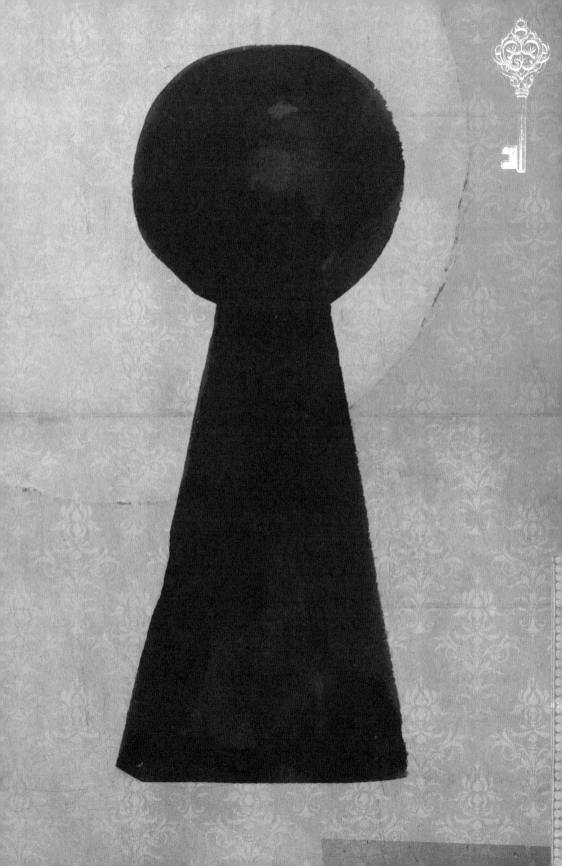

THANK you So So So much:

To my agent SURESH, whose patience and perseverance knows no bounds

To my EDITOR Nicki and the whole team at FRANCES LINCOLN, whose vision and passion for this book has made it possible.

To Mum and Dad, James and Olivia, my wonderful Grandparents and extended family for your continued love and support

To Rachel for your brilliant mind

To Chris, Jonathan, Gary and Phil at The University of the West of England. I owe you so much

To Brittany and the boys in Bristol

To Alex, Duncan, Abbie and all my friends and colleagues at Greenshaw High School

To my family at Carshalton Beeches Baptist Church

5

Frances Lincoln Limited
74–77 White Lion Street, London N1 9PF
www.franceslincoln.com

Collage and Keep: A creative journal inspired by your life
Copyright © Frances Lincoln Limited 2015
Text and artwork copyright © Eleanor Shakespeare 2015

First Frances Lincoln edition 2015

A catalogue record for this book is available from the British Library.

978-0-7112-3735-3

Printed and bound in China

1 2 3 4 5 6 7 8 9